Copyright © 1977 by Grisewood & Dempsey Ltd.
First published in USA 1984 by Exeter Books.
Distributed by Bookthrift.
Exeter is a trademark of Simon & Schuster, Inc.
Bookthrift is a registered trademark of
Simon & Schuster, Inc., New York, New York.

ISBN 0-671-07180-7

Printed and bound in Portugal by Printer Portuguesa, Sintra.

The Mouse

By Angela Sheehan
Illustrated by Maurice Pledger

Exeter Books

NEW YORK

It was a warm, windy night. Clouds covered
the moon and stars, and hid their light. It
was so dark that even an owl could not see
the mouse as she scratched among the leaves.
The mouse was safe.

She ate some grass shoots and insects.
Then she ran along the path to the nest where
her five babies were sleeping. As she ran,
the clouds suddenly drifted away from the
moon and its light shone on the mouse. Now
she was in danger. A weasel caught sight of
her. The mouse hid behind a clump of grass.
Without moving, she watched the weasel as it
tried to find her again.

The wind blew. The grass wavered. And
the light shone. The mouse stroked her whiskers
in terror. But the weasel could no longer see
her. After a while it went away. Safe again,
the mouse hurried home.

Deep inside the burrow, the babies were safe and warm. Most of the time they slept or sucked milk from their mother. Soon they would have to learn how to find their own food and how to escape all the enemies that lived in the woods.

As soon as the young mice could move about, they explored the long tunnels in their burrow. Sometimes they peeped out of the entrance holes to see what the world was like. But it was some time before they dared to go out.

The first time they went out, the mice followed their mother a little way. Then an owl hooted and the whole family fled back to the nest.

The young mice did not feel safe in the woods. The strange new smells and sounds frightened them. They could smell all kinds of plants and animals. And there was so much noise that they had to listen really hard to hear the squeaks of their nest mates.

After a few days, the young mice grew
less afraid. But they were still careful
when they went out alone. All kinds of
animals were ready to pounce on them at their
first careless squeak or movement. So the
mice learned to run quickly and quietly, and
to hide when the moon shone too brightly.

Soon they left their mother's nest and
dug new burrows for themselves.

But they were not all lucky enough to escape their enemies. One young mouse was killed by a weasel that sneaked into his burrow. Another two were caught on different nights by a tawny owl.

The mother mouse did not know what was happening to her young. She stayed in her burrow each day as usual, and went out to find food at night.

One night she heard the sound of another mouse as she was scratching about by a hawthorn tree. The mouse was a large male that lived by the roots of the tree. The two animals sniffed at each other until they felt that they knew each other well. Then they mated.

Afterwards, they both ran back to the safety of their burrows.

Three weeks and three days after she had mated, the mother mouse gave birth to six babies. They were her third family that summer. The babies were small and pink. They could not hear or see. All they could do was suck milk and squeak. But soon their fur grew thick and their big black eyes opened.

Their mother often left them curled up together while she went out for food. One night she stayed out so long that it was almost morning when she set out for home.

Her hungry babies were waiting for her, so the mouse ran as quickly as she could. As she came near the nest she saw a fearful sight. Her burrow was in ruins. Soil from the tunnels and grass from the nest was scattered everywhere. A badger's footprints led from the burrow.

The mouse turned away. She knew that
all her babies were dead. And she knew that
she would be dead, too, if she did not quickly
find a place to hide.

She looked around for a hideout and found
a rotting log by the side of the stream. The
wood had crumbled into holes. The mouse
tried one with her whiskers to see if she
would fit inside it. It was just big enough,
so she squeezed her way in. She curled her
tail round her body, and went slowly to sleep.

When she woke up again, it was night.
She looked and listened for enemies. All was
silent and safe, but she dared not go far
from her hideout. Quickly she made a hole in
the bank below the log. She would dig a new
burrow just there.

Digging with her front paws, she soon
made a tunnel about three times as long as
her body. At the end she scooped out a hole.
Then she ran back to the entrance to clear
the soil away. Lastly she dragged some grass
into the hole to line it.

Digging tunnels was hard work for the
mouse, After she had made the first one, she
rested. Then she dug another. All night she
worked, until she had made four strong tunnels.
By morning, she had a home where she could
raise a new family. First she must find a new
mate. But before that, she needed to sleep.

It was dark when she woke and she was
hungry. The woods were full of food. There
were berries, grasses, seeds, roots, toadstools,
slugs, snails, and tasty insects. She ate some
and carried some back to her nest for a store.
A few days later, she hid a pile of berries in
a hole nearby. Every night she ate and
collected more and more.

One night she went to the hazel tree.
She loved the taste of hazel nuts and gnawed
at them hungrily. She did not notice that
another mouse was listening to her noisy
gnawing. It was the same mouse that she had
met by the hawthorn. He, too, had come to
collect hazel nuts.

He hid behind a tree when he heard her.
Then he peeped out to see what the noise was.
When he saw the female mouse, he scampered
over to her, and they mated again.

Just over three weeks later, the mouse gave birth to another family. This time there were five babies. The weather was growing cold and windy now. The mouse mostly stayed in the nest, where she had nuts and berries to eat. Her babies grew quickly. It was not long before they were able to eat the softer berries, and wash their own fur and whiskers. They raced up and down the tunnels or played together on the bank outside the nest.

One night there was a terrible storm.
Bright lights flashed across the sky and lit
up the trees. Rain poured down. All the
animals were scared. A great clap of thunder
made a herd of deer panic. They ran blindly
in all directions.

One headed for the bank where the mice
lived. His hoof hit the log above the burrow.
The log slipped down the bank, and carried
the nest and all the young mice with it.

The wet mice squeaked with fear as the water in the stream swirled round them. They were too young to swim. They held on to clumps of grass, while their mother tried to save them. She scrambled on to the bank and reached out to drag them from the water. Two of the mice were out of reach. They were swept away by the flood as she pulled the other three out.

The mother mouse left the three wet mice on the bank, while she went off to find a dry hole. She found one in a tree stump and then hurried back to lead the babies to safety.

By morning the storm was over, but the ground was still wet and muddy. Broken branches and leaves lay everywhere. The mouse made her way through them back to her burrow. Happily only part of it had been destroyed. So she started to repair it, digging deeper into the bank and collecting new grass.

When she had finished, she led her babies back to the nest. But still she could not rest. All the nuts and berries in her food store had been scattered. She must find them all and bring them back. She ran back and forth, picking up the nuts and berries. She worked until she was too tired to go on.

The nest was now as good as new, but before long it was time for the young mice to leave. They soon stopped drinking their mother's milk. And at night they went out on their own.

When they left for good, the weather was much colder. So they dug new burrows where they could hide from the wind and the rain, as well as from their enemies. Most of them tunneled into the ground. But one mouse found an empty bird's nest in a holly bush. It was big enough for her and a stock of berries. She would be safe there for the winter. In spring, she would be able to raise a family there.

During the winter it was so cold that the mother mouse stayed home for most of the time. She slept more now. Even when snow covered the ground above, the burrow was warm. She did not need much food because she had eaten so much in the fall.

One day she was wakened from her sleep by a scratching noise coming from her food store. She ran down the tunnel, and discovered a squirrel stealing her nuts. The squirrels never remembered where they buried their own nuts. So they just stole any they found.

The mouse waited until the squirrel had eaten enough nuts and gone back to its tree. Then she hid the few that were left and closed up the hole in the burrow. She did not really need the nuts. Now her family had gone, she had little to do but find food.

But as winter wore on, there was less and less food in the woods. And more animals were looking for it. Strange mice were even coming into the woods from the fields, now that food there was scarce. All the animals were hungry, except those lucky enough to be asleep under the ground.

The woodland stayed cold for months.
Then new shoots sprang up, flowers bloomed,
and insects crawled over the floor. There
would be a lot of food for the mouse in the
warm, sunny months to come.

More About Mice

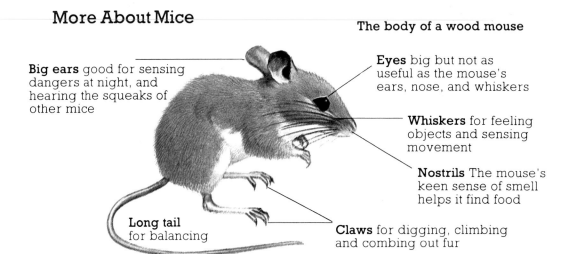

The body of a wood mouse

Big ears good for sensing dangers at night, and hearing the squeaks of other mice

Eyes big but not as useful as the mouse's ears, nose, and whiskers

Whiskers for feeling objects and sensing movement

Nostrils The mouse's keen sense of smell helps it find food

Long tail for balancing

Claws for digging, climbing and combing out fur

Mice belong to a group of animals called rodents. Rodents are animals that gnaw. They have large chisel-shaped front teeth. These teeth are worn down all the time as the animal gnaws. But they never stop growing.

The mouse in the story is the wood mouse. It is related to other kinds of mice as well as to rats, squirrels, voles, guinea pigs and beavers. Its body is four inches long and its tail is as long again.

A Mouse's House

The wood mouse's burrow is a network of tunnels with a "nursery" for the young and "storerooms" for food. The entrances are little more than an inch wide. From them, lead routes which the mice follow

"nursery"

food store

A wood mouse's burrow. It is about $1\frac{1}{2}$ yards from side to side

over and over when they go out for food.

The wood mouse keeps its nest and its body as clean as possible. It combs its fur with its claws.

More and More Mice

The wood mouse has as many as five families each year with up to six babies in each. The babies are suckled by their mother for three weeks after they are born. They grow quickly. At five months they are ready to breed them-selves. They live for about two years, if they are not killed sooner.

Enemies Everywhere

Wherever mice live they are in danger. People kill them because they steal food. And they are a favorite food of meat eating animals. Owls are their chief enemies.

The wood mouse can run fast to escape its enemies. It can jump more than a yard. But it is not safe, even in its nest.

House mouse

Yellow-necked mouse

Harvest mouse

Dormouse

Edible dormouse

**Some other kinds of mice. They all have similar tracks.
The dormice are only distant cousins of the other three**